OUR GARDEN BOOK
was conceived and edited
by Imogen Bright and
Vanessa Whinney,
Eyebright Publications,
21 Weedon Lane,
Amersham,
Bucks HP6 5QT.

Designers: Anthony
Lawrence and Hilly Beavan
Artist: Jenny Norton
Text: M.J. Brazier

First published 1987
© Eyebright Publications,
1987

Typeset by Bookworm,
Manchester
Printed and bound in Hong
Kong by Mandarin Offset

ISBN 0 948751 01 0

OUR
GARDEN BOOK

THE GARDEN PLANNER AND RECORD KEEPER

CONTENTS

HOW TO USE THIS BOOK

The purpose of this book is to help you to achieve the garden of your dreams. It will enable you to create and plan a more rewarding and enjoyable garden without necessarily having to do a lot of extra work. You can also have the added pleasure of recording the results of your efforts.

The secret of success consists partly in developing your existing garden, and partly in careful planning. The best results can be obtained by introducing a few new ideas or improvements each year, and by making sure that the right job gets done at the right time.

This highly practical book can be used by all gardeners to build up more effective and consistent results over the years. Following a few introductory pages of general helpful advice there are three sections for you to write in. The Inventory, the Planner and the Monthly Notes sections provide a simple and clear structure for building up a complete plan and record of your garden. If you use these sections as suggested, the book will become your personal and invaluable garden manual. What you write will help you to develop a beautiful and productive garden.

INVENTORY

The Inventory section will provide you with a permanent record of the current contents of your garden. Its purpose is to serve as a basis for future planning. Enter the names, characteristics and requirements of your plants; details of permanent features such as paths, sheds and lawns; lists of tools, suppliers and books. You can also use these pages to note ideas gleaned from radio or television, hints from magazine articles, or names of plants seen in other people's gardens. Keep the Inventory up to date by entering any alterations, plants acquired or plants you wish to acquire.

Once you have filled in this section, use the information for organising the next year's work in the Planner section. These notes will be very useful when choosing new plants, and when trying to remember the names of plants which have lost their labels, or died down and disappeared.

PLANNER

The purpose of the Planner section is to help you to develop a programme for improving your garden. If properly used, it will transform your garden into one that is stunningly beautiful and productive. Use what you write in the Inventory and the Monthly Notes as the basis for your planning in this section. It is fun to try to include something new in your garden each year. Aim to extend the flowering period, to increase fresh produce, or to disguise an ugly corner.

Decide when you need to do the work, and make the appropriate entries under the correct month. If you are growing vegetables or flowers from seed, a systematic sowing plan will help to bring success. Refer back to the Inventory to ensure that you provide for the needs of individual plants each month, and that you do not neglect more general maintenance. Don't forget to list those boring, but necessary regular jobs, such as weeding and spraying which, if done at the right time, will greatly improve your garden. When you have completed a job, make a note of the date and year.

You can refer back to the Planner when writing up the Monthly Notes section. You will find that this information becomes increasingly valuable over the years in helping you to achieve ever more impressive results.

MONTHLY NOTES

The purpose of the Monthly Notes is to allow you to sit back and judge the results of your labours and to develop your ideas. After all your planning and hard work, did the results match your expectations? What did you most enjoy in your garden? This is the section where you record what you actually achieved during the year.

Use it as a diary to describe how your garden looked and what it produced. The marginal text is intended to make you look carefully and critically at your garden month by month, and to stimulate ideas. Note any failures, gaps or mistakes as well as successes, and then make suggested improvements for the future. Refer to the Planner in order to assess accurately if your sowing, planting, feeding and pruning were done at the right time, and if they produced the desired results.

You should also use this section as a way of simply enjoying and appreciating your garden. You will be amazed to discover the variations and contrasts which occur from year to year, and it is good to indulge in a little self-congratulation. Finally, make use of these valuable notes when filling in the Planner for the following year.

"Planning, projecting, imagining are the very soul of gardening."

From Hugh Johnson's introduction to *The Garden*, published in conjunction with the exhibition at the Victoria and Albert Museum, London, 1979.

WHY HAVE A GARDEN?

Since the beginning of time man has tilled the soil and cultivated plants in order to provide food for his survival. With today's abundance of supermarkets, ease of access to fresh produce and ready availability of take-away foods, it is interesting to consider what it is that drives people to work long, strenuous hours creating and maintaining a garden.

Many home-owners feel that a beautiful garden which enhances the house is as important as the interior furnishings, and will willingly strive to obtain the best possible results themselves or pay professionals to do the work. In many instances from the smallest cottage to the largest estate, there is an inherent pride and joy in making the most of all available ground. But for most of us there is something more vital involved.

Gardening is a wonderfully creative hobby. Out of chaos and desolation one can establish beauty, order and pleasure. A subtle blend of colours, scents, textures and foliages presenting interest and fascination, combined with visual and nasal delights, are probably the highest achievements possible. The very fact that no real gardener has ever been known to rest on his laurels proves that the challenge to create a higher standard of perfection is always present.

Ecologists and conservationists are keenly aware that having a garden presents them with the opportunity to encourage and support wildlife by creating the right environment for animals and insects to live in. Over the years man has done so much to destroy the natural habitat of our wildlife that it will take many years to redress the balance of nature. From very small beginnings more and more families are trying to create individual conservation areas in private gardens, and thereby gaining great pleasure and encouragement.

For some people gardening is all about the fascination of having one's hands in the soil and working with living, growing plants. There is something very soothing and rewarding in preparing the soil, planting a minute seed and then sitting back to watch the magic of a young plant emerging and establishing itself. Some gardeners become specialists in individual subjects ranging from miniature alpines to giant cacti, while others dream of, and strive to produce, a completely new strain or variation of an existing species. Anyone who has taken a cutting, watched it take root and eventually flower, will long to propagate his or her favourite plants and re-stock the garden. It is the very diversity of gardening skills and occupations which lures so many people into becoming gardeners.

For those living within the confines of a nine-to-five existence in the concrete jungle of office blocks, it is

not surprising that many workers revel in outdoor living at the weekends and seize every opportunity to commune with nature in their own gardens. Sun worshippers, barbeque lovers and weary weekenders all feel refreshed and rejuvenated by two days spent in the garden.

For families and pet lovers gardens have three important functions – somewhere to dry the laundry, somewhere safe for the children to play and enjoy the fresh air, and somewhere to exercise the dog, cat or rabbit. These may sound extraordinary reasons for having a garden, but statistics show that they are the three features most missed by flat dwellers. Depending on the age of the children, most gardens evolve through the stages of being a pram and nappy repository, a swing and slide provider, a football and cricket pitch and finally a barbeque and sunbathing haven.

The pride and joy resulting from growing fresh fruit and vegetables must be experienced to be fully appreciated. Once you have enjoyed picking succulent, crisp peas just prior to eating them, or collected a really generous helping of sun-warmed raspberries heavy with fragrance, then by comparison, buying produce at the supermarket is very second-rate. It takes a certain amount of hard work to produce a constant supply of vegetables, but the pleasure involved and the fulfilling sense of achievement are more than adequate reward. Previously, one could usually grow only one fruit tree in an average garden, but with modern technology and dwarf rooting stocks it takes very little ingenuity to grow a good variety of bushes in fascinating cordons, espaliers and multiple-fruiting trees. Some gardeners delight in growing an abundance of highly expensive crops such as asparagus or artichokes, and indulge their palates for comparitively little cost.

The thriving economy of the cut flower industry bears witness to the homemaker's love of using flowers to decorate the home. For some, there is the fascination of formal arrangements or exotic Japanese creations, while for others there is the delight of extending the natural simplicity of the garden by bringing indoors a subtle blending of outdoor colour and fragrance.

Few people would make a garden with the sole purpose of using it as something to share, but inevitably gardeners are great sharers. Is there such a thing as a gardener who does not like to show off his garden, to invite someone in, no matter how awful it may be? As a topic of conversation gardening is second to none – as any non-gardener will soon tell you! When not actually discussing the subject themselves, gardeners are fascinated by lectures, television programmes and horticultural shows, and soon find common interests with their fellow enthusiasts. Enormous pleasure is derived from the exchange of seeds, seedlings or cuttings. Sharing may not be the initial reason for having a garden, but it is certainly one of the greatest pleasures.

Involvement in an occupation that has so many facets and which is never stationary is physically and mentally stimulating. The challenges presented by the weather, and the tangible sense of evolution, progress and continuity are eminently pleasing. Gardeners spend a good deal of time making plans and there is something very special about watching those plans come to fruition. Over the years one comes to appreciate the inevitable unfolding and development of living things. One constantly marvels at the infinite scope of colour, beauty, delicacy and sheer fascination which a garden produces. There can surely be few hobbies as rewarding and satisfying as having a garden.

IMPROVING YOUR GARDEN

Does your garden conjure up pictures of elegant lawns and neatly trimmed hedges while terraces and flower beds unfold a continuous blaze of colour, or is it untidy, overcrowded and rather dull with scraggy clumps of colour? Before rushing in and attempting to make drastic changes, it is worth making a systematic plan.

Try to live with the garden as it is for a year. Discover what is already growing well, take regular photographs and make a few notes and sketches. Do you most desire lawns for the children to play on, sheltered areas for sunbathing, terraces for outdoor eating, or just a beautiful garden? Evaluate the needs of the family and the use to be made of the garden, and then start planning accordingly.

Before you start to make changes, it is also wise to consider how much time you have available for regular gardening. The layout of the garden as well as the plants you grow there will determine the amount of work required. Calculate the relative costs involved in purchasing annuals and bedding plants together with the amount of time it will take to plant them out each year, and compare that with the initial outlay in time and money needed to establish a perennial or a shrub garden which requires minimum maintenance. Explore the implications of growing more fruit and vegetables. Learning to take cuttings and to save your own seeds are pleasurable and economical ways of re-stocking your garden.

In order to grow well most plants need sunlight. Seriously consider your garden in relation to north, south, east and west, and the amount of sun or shade that each bed receives. Are your existing plants suitably placed? A magnificent flowering shrub in your neighbour's garden, grown in the ideal place, will never produce the same glory in your garden if it is given the wrong aspect. Get to know the needs of individual plants; study the ideal conditions required by any plant which shows poor growth, and be prepared to move it at the right time.

It is essential to know the type of soil in your garden. Before choosing new plants have a look at local gardens, and learn from their successes which plants will thrive in the prevailing weather and soil conditions.

Probably the single most important thing you can do to improve a garden is to build a large, efficient compost heap. All plants respond to proper care, and while chemicals will feed the soil and peat will improve the texture, compost will enrich and improve both soil and texture at no extra cost. Ideally, there should be one compost heap maturing while the second one is being built. This will ensure a constant supply of well-rotted material.

Similarly, all plants respond to careful watering. Haphazard, surface dampening will only encourage roots to come to the surface, thus jeopardising the health of plants which need to establish a deeply growing, moist and food-searching root system.

Fifteen minutes weeding or hoeing daily to control annual weeds such as chickweed and groundsel before they flower and produce seed is far more effective than a full day's onslaught once a month. Perennial weeds such as couch grass and ground elder are extraordinarily tenacious, and are best controlled with chemical weed killers. Weeds are notoriously healthy growers, and if they are not removed frequently they soon rob the soil of nourishment intended for your plants.

Many of our smaller town gardens seem to have a disproportionately large amount of hedge when it comes to hedge cutting. The overall beauty of most gardens is closely linked to the height, density and appearance of the hedges. Occasional thinning and pruning will be well rewarded, as will an annual cleaning out of the matted mess at the roots, where pest and insects spend the winter, followed by a stimulating feed.

Lawns help to set the tone of a garden. Regular mowing and edge trimming will encourage improvement, but if you take the trouble to rake, spike and top-dress the lawn in early autumn, and you are prepared to re-seed bare patches or re-turf unsightly edges, provided the drainage is reasonably good, your lawn will soon enhance your garden.

With the wide variety of fruit trees and bushes as well as vegetable seedlings readily available, many gardeners choose to grow their own fruit and vegetables. Eating home-grown produce is enormously rewarding. Ideally, a separate area of the garden can be set aside for this, but in a small garden a little ingenuity will enable you to grow runner beans at the back of the flower bed, tomatoes amongst the roses and lettuces between the annuals, while cordons of apples, gooseberries and blackberries grown on a wall or fence will provide many a delicious meal. Herbs add beauty and fragrance to any garden as well as being delicious in cooking and beneficial for your health.

Innovation is the secret of successful gardening. Take the plunge and be prepared to make some changes once you have decided on both the needs and the possibilities of your garden. It may be the introduction of new plants, the design of a new bed, the inclusion of a path or a pool, or it may be a completely different layout incorporating fresh features or special areas for nature conservation, a children's garden or a corner for unusual plants.

The real purpose of a garden is to give pleasure. It should be both stimulating and rewarding, but never a burden. It is possible to provide instant colour by spending a lot of money at a garden centre. However, by following the foregoing notes you can greatly improve your garden, increase the value of your property, and create a beautiful, established garden which will bless you and the neighbourhood. Try it!

ARMCHAIR GARDENING

There comes a time during the winter months when even the most ardent gardener is confined to the home by lack of daylight and atrocious weather. For some it is a time of frustration and boredom, but for real enthusiasts those long winter evenings are a glorious opportunity to indulge in armchair gardening. One finally has time to settle down and enjoy all those garden catalogues, magazines and books which have been piling up, without feeling guilty about unmown lawns or overgrown weeds.

With so much expert information readily available, it is enormously helpful to make full use of the materials and time at your disposal from the depth of a comfortable armchair. Pictures and illustrations are an abundant source of inspiration – for more pleasing shapes and contents of flower beds, a changed garden layout, or for the introduction of completely new ideas. Read up those notes jotted down while listening to a radio or television programme, or look at the rough plans and sketches you made while visiting a famous garden. Gradually you will start making lists of possible changes you would like to make in your garden next year – discarding some old friends, introducing a new feature, experimenting with different varieties of flowers and vegetables – and generally opening your thoughts to fresh visions.

Seed catalogues can be stimulating reading matter! Those exquisite miniature photographs convince even the most experienced gardeners that growing from seed is absolutely foolproof. Glorious sights are envisioned and mighty decisions are made as the new seed order develops. Purchasing seeds from a catalogue is often cheaper than buying odd packets in a shop, and if you belong to an allotment or horticultural society or a local garden club whereby you can purchase in bulk, the cost is considerably reduced. Some seed merchants give an additional reduction if orders are placed before 1st January.

When the seeds finally arrive remember to mark the year of purchase on the packet. This will avoid the frustration of sowing old seeds which fail to germinate. It is a good idea, while you have the time and energy, to draw up a chronological monthly sowing plan. (The Planner section of this book gives you the opportunity to record which seeds must be sown month by month.) If you tie the seed packets into separate bundles for each month, you will save endless time searching for illusive packets once the busy planting season begins.

During the active gardening months there is seldom time to research why things go wrong or why failures occur. Winter evenings provide an opportunity to remedy this. In the Monthly Notes section you can note down the problems as they occur and

find out the reasons later – what are the ideal soil and weather conditions, is special feeding or pruning required, or does the plant have a unique, hitherto unknown, need? Having found the solutions, it only takes a moment to record them in the relevant section for the future.

Most gardening skills are acquired through trial and error and in conversation with other gardeners. However, a little time spent over the winter reading from the huge variety of gardening books and magazines available will repay large dividends. It will not only increase your knowledge and improve your technique in propagating, layering, pruning etc., but you will also be able to catch up on the latest innovations and inventions in the gardening world.

Planning is an important, though time-consuming, element of gardening. The greatest joy of armchair planning is that with very little effort you can change your mind and your plans as often as you like until you reach the perfect arrangement. The most detailed planning usually involves the rotation of crops plan and the annual feeding of the flower beds. The three main forms of soil nutrient replenishment are well-rotted organic compost, manure and chemicals. Cultivation is made much easier if vegetables which require similar feeding are grown together. In order to get the best results, the feeding pattern and the crops grown on each area of the vegetable patch should be changed every year. Similarly, it is customary to grow lime-hating plants together in one area of the flower garden where they can be well isolated.

There are certain other routine jobs which demand careful planning. The more carefully and precisely the planning is done in the winter months, the better the execution of the plans will be, and consequently the results achieved will be more impressive. These jobs include the annual spray programme for fruit crops, the control and destruction of regular pests on plants such as roses, and the monthly care and maintenance of lawns and hedges. Because a job done at the right time is always more effective than spasmodic bursts of activity, this form of armchair planning is most worthwhile.

The winter months provide a good opportunity to complete unfinished entries in diaries and logbooks such as this one, to look back at the records kept, and to review the successes of the previous season. Many of these entries will help to establish a pattern of gardening over the years which will greatly improve your garden. Look forward also to next year and note the dates of the specialist shows of your favourite plants.

Armchair gardening is, above all else, a wonderful time to sit and dream. Make the most of it, because when the grass starts to grow, the weeds double overnight, the seedlings need pricking out, and the whole garden needs watering, there is not going to be too much time to sit around comfortably dreaming.

WILDLIFE IN THE GARDEN

It is well known that many wildlife habitats are disappearing at an alarming rate, thanks to increasing human activity. A striking exception is the garden habitat, which thrives and expands in spite of growing pressures. Individual gardens are just minute oases amid the bricks and mortar, but overall they form a substantial nature reserve. Although modern technology and horticultural fashions are detrimental to wildlife, if we can encourage more people to adopt natural gardening methods and to respect unfamiliar plants, then we can actively tempt wildlife, evicted from elsewhere, into our gardens.

A wildlife garden is not a garden which is neglected and has run wild. It is a garden that has been thoughtfully and lovingly planned to support and increase wildlife. With a very few exceptions, this can be done without detriment to either the beauty or the productivity of your garden. The many different parts of the garden – walls, fences, trees, hedges, paths, lawns as well as the cultivated areas – all provide homes for animals and insects. The greater the diversity and the wider the variety of plants grown, including weeds, the larger the resulting wildlife population will be.

The importance of maintaining a garden by natural means wherever possible cannot be over-emphasized. The modern trend for instant action inveigles gardeners into using poisons, insecticides, weed-killers and aerosol sprays with little thought for the resulting devastation of the balance of nature. How often does the thoughtless use of a pesticide, applied to aphids during the hours of bright sunlight, kill off the bees which are busy pollinating the flowers? Promoting an increase of ladybirds and the tolerance of ants, both of which eat aphids, or "companion planting" in the vegetable patch, would be much more beneficial.

Basic garden wisdom demands the constant improvement and replenishment of the soil. It is all too easy to apply chemical fertilisers. But it is much better in the long term to make a compost heap where worms and insects can breed and flourish. If you have a vegetable or fruit garden where plants are frequently removed from the ground, it is particularly important that organic matter in the form of rotted compost be replaced in the soil. Compost will ensure the survival of creepy crawlies in the soil, and hence better soil texture and healthy growth of the next crop. If you use a hoe for weeding, you will provide decaying vegetable matter for insects and nutrients for the soil. This is infinitely more desirable than weedkillers, which kill indescriminately and subsequently harm the texture and content of the soil.

Bird gardening is undoubtedly the most widely practised form of wildlife gardening. To increase the varieties of birds visiting a garden you can provide trees and shrubs for perching and cover. A really dense clump of greenery will attract robins, chaffinches and dunnocks. Fruit and seed-bearing plants will tempt bird palates, and few vegetarian birds can resist berries on bushes and trees – holly, cotoneaster, berberis, pyracantha or rowan. Teasels will draw goldfinches like magnets. An old, rotting piece of wood, sprouting fungi and bacteria, will soon be covered with insects, much to the delight of insectivorous birds, which thrive on worms, slugs and caterpillars. A good bird book will tell you which plants to grow to tempt specific birds to take up residence.

Bird tables bedecked with scraps, unwanted fat, bird seed or rotting fruit are always rewarded with hungry visitors, and regular replenishment will bring regular callers, particularly in winter when supplementary food is essential. During freezing spells birds are dependent for survival on fresh supplies of food and water daily. The correct placing of the right-sized nesting box will ultimately encourage breeding, and bring to the garden all the delights of watching a young family being reared.

Many are the nocturnal creatures which we never actually see, but which benefit greatly if we do a little bit of special preparation for them in the garden. Areas of long grass, sited amongst the exposed roots of a tree, provide a suitable habitat for the long-tailed field or wood mouse who make their nests in a hole in the ground. Hips from the rose bush or haws from the hawthorne hedge will also prove an irresistible attraction. The hedgehog is a universal pest controller, delighting in insects, larvae, slugs – and the odd saucer of milk. It thrives in an herbaceous border that is allowed to have clumps of dead leaves around and, as its name suggests, it frequents hedges. With the loss of hedgerows in the countryside, hedges provide rich habitats for plants and animals.

Butterflies and moths bring beauty and enchantment to any garden, and are easily encouraged. Their greatest requirement is food, particularly nectar. Unfortunately modern technology produces magnificent specimens of hybrid flowers totally lacking in nectar and scent. Our winged friends need the old-fashioned cottage garden flowers – wallflowers, sedum, perennial yellow alyssum, honesty, pink thrift and buddleia. Healthy nettles for the leaf-eating caterpillars, and docks and dead nettles for the moth caterpillars, ensure that the life cycle will continue.

The introduction of a pond brings a whole new dimension to wildlife gardening. Careful stocking will encourage the normal sorts of invertebrates – pondskater, dragonfly, whirleygig beetle and mayfly. Aim to include amphibians as well – frogs, toads and lizards, whose habitats are vanishing fast. Birds will come to paddle in the shallow edges of a pond and fish will breed in deeper waters.

Wildlife gardening is all about choosing the right plants, growing them in the most natural and advantageous way, not being fanatical about neatness and tidyness, and allowing wildlife simply to flourish and increase. A well-established balance of wildlife tends to control itself, and interestingly, far less time will be spent by the gardener on pest control – one blue tit family will consume seven thousand caterpillars! In an increasingly ecology-conscious society it is almost our duty to develop and use our gardens as nature reserves. We should aim to conserve the natural history which is such a vital part of our heritage.

This section will provide you with a permanent record of the current contents of your garden. The purpose of the Inventory is to serve as a basis for future planning. Enter the names, characteristics and requirements of your plants; details of permanent features such as paths, sheds and lawns; lists of tools, suppliers and books. You can also use these pages to note ideas gleaned from radio or television, hints from magazine articles, or names of plants seen in other people's gardens. Keep the Inventory up to date by entering any alterations, plants acquired or plants you wish to acquire. Once you have filled in this section, use the information for organising the next year's work in the Planner section. Refer to these pages when choosing new plants, and when trying to remember the names of plants which have lost their labels.

INVENTORY

FRONT GARDEN

Use this page to record the basic information about your front garden. Making a list of its characteristics will help you to understand its potential and its problem places. You will then have a good starting point for future plans. Draw a plan (do a rough first) marking in the main features – boundaries, terrace, lawns, large trees, buildings, flower beds, produce beds, access and paths, waterbutts, hose points, compost, etc. Identify the beds with a letter or number. Use this plan for marking in the position of individual plants when you are completing the rest of this section. Give each plant a key number. Refer back to this page when you subsequently do any planting. You will find it very helpful when you are using the Planner section or dreaming about innovations. For further hints on filling up this page, see over.

Size

Soil type

Aspect

Shady

Sunny

Drainage

Notes

B A C K   G A R D E N

Record here the basic information about your back garden (and if applicable, your side garden) in the same way as suggested on the previous page. If you do your drawing in pencil, you can put in any alterations that you make to your garden in the future. Use the grid on pages 102-3 for making new plans. Start by measuring your garden, and enter the dimensions below. Carry out a soil test to find out which plants are most suited to the conditions. Note which areas are in sun or shade to enable you to position plants correctly. The quality of drainage can be crucial in creating a successful garden. Under the Notes heading, write down points such as ownership of boundary fences and hedges, trees with preservation orders and legal regulations. Your sketch will be helpful when you are using the Planner section or dreaming about innovations. Labels get lost easily, and it is often hard to remember the details and positions of plants, especially in winter when everything dies down, and you are not sure where to place new plants.

Size

Soil type

Aspect

Shady

Sunny

Drainage

Notes

23

MAJOR JOBS DONE

This page can be a particularly satisfying part of the book. You will find it very encouraging to watch how a garden grows and develops over the years, and to recall what you have achieved. List here the dates and details of major jobs undertaken as well as alterations in design and structure. Note the introduction of new features, showing the joyful evolution of your garden. Make sketches or add them to the plans on pages 20 and 22.

T R E E S ,   S H R U B S   &   H E D G E S

Trees, shrubs and hedges help to give character to a garden. With good design they can provide interesting shapes and textures all the year round. Choose them for their decorative effects, colours and contrasts, and use them to form barriers or screens. Trees and shrubs normally require little attention, and the main tasks are pruning and feeding. Hedges need to be cut twice a year. Enter details of the trees, shrubs and hedges in your garden, following the pattern of the sample headings given. Mark their positions on your plans on pages 20 and 22, using a key number. Fill in the Planner section also as a reminder of when care is required, because correct maintenance at the right time doubles the beauty of any plant.

Name

Source

Date planted/Position/Key no.

Height/Colour/In flower

Feeding/Pruning time

Special needs

TREES, SHRUBS & HEDGES

Continue to enter details
of the trees, shrubs and
hedges in your garden, as
suggested on the
previous page.

INVENTORY · TREES, SHRUBS & HEDGES

Herbaceous flower beds are a glorious sight in a garden. They offer endless possibilities for great beauty, especially if thoughtfully planned. Consider carefully the size and shape of your beds, using curves where possible. Vary the height, width, density and texture of plants, and aim for continuity of constantly changing colour. Regular weeding, feeding, staking, dividing and replanting helps to ensure success. Record here your existing plants and any new additions, using the sample headings given for guidance. Give each plant a key number, and then mark them on your plans. Use the Planner and Monthly Notes to expand and extend flowering possibilities.

Name

Source

Date planted/Position/Key no.

Height/Colour/In flower

Special needs

HERBACEOUS PLANTS

Use these pages to list
your herbaceous plants,
using the headings
suggested on the
previous page.

_____

_____

_____

_____

_____

_____

_____

_____

_____

_____

_____

_____

_____

_____

_____

_____

_____

_____

_____

_____

_____

_____

_____

_____

R O S E S

Name

Source

Date planted/Position/Key no.

Height/Colour/In flower

Feeding/Pruning time

Special needs

For many gardeners roses take pride of place. They enhance any garden whether grown in individual beds or amongst other flowers. With their wide range of colours and fragrances, ramblers, climbers, floribundas, hybrid teas, standards and miniatures epitomize the full glory of June. A little forethought will enable you to extend their flowering period. Mulching, feeding, disbudding and pruning, with careful winter and summer pest control, will bring endless rewards. Effective use of the Planner will prevent forgotten tasks. Use this page to enter essential information about the roses in your garden, as indicated by the sample headings. Mark their positions on your plans (pages 20 and 22), using a key number so that you do not confuse their names. Careful entries in the Monthly Notes will show where additions or changes are needed.

BULBS & CORMS

After the deadness of winter, bulbs herald the coming of spring. Let this page account for that first glory. Grown in clumps, in empty flower beds, or naturalised in the grass, daffodils, crocuses and chionodoxas brighten the dullest day. Don't forget that you can grow many beautiful varieties in summer, autumn and winter as well as in spring. List the names and details of all your bulbs, corms and tubers in the way suggested by the sample headings , and mark their position on your plans, using a key number. This will help you to avoid damage after the foliage has disappeared. When shortages of bulbs become apparent, add a reminder in the Planner to order and replant.

Name

Source

Date planted/Position/Key no.

Height/Colour/In flower

Special needs

Whether you grow them from seed or purchase them from a garden centre, annuals and bedding plants transform a garden. They provide instant and prolonged colour, are useful for filling gaps or tubs, and are a grand source of cut flowers for the house. List here your favourite flowers, preferably in well-tried combinations, and add comments on their cultivation. Timing is essential in sowing seed, purchasing seedlings, hardening off and planting out. Try one or two new plants each year, and exclude repeated failures. To avoid such failures, use the Planner, outlining the correct sequence of jobs to be done. Your garden will improve from year to year if you account for results in the Monthly Notes.

The fascination of an ideal garden lies in the element of surprise. Special garden areas offer a splendid opportunity to cultivate different types of plants and to encourage wildlife. Use this page to describe the special areas in your garden – scented garden, butterfly garden, wild garden, water garden, children's garden, rockery, etc. List the plants which you grow there and the special care they require. Note the additions and improvements which you make. The possibilities are infinite for giving your imagination free rein, and for creating beautiful and unusual corners.

C O N T A I N E R S

What an opportunity containers present to the imaginative gardener! Experiment with hanging baskets planted with trailing blossoms, old kitchen sinks filled with miniature alpines, or window boxes overflowing with annuals. Use tubs at the front door for anything from bay trees to standard fuchsias. Here is a creative way to extend a small garden, to introduce a new feature, to grow unusual plants, or just to be wildly outrageous. Note the containers you have, what plants you regularly grow in them and their cultivation. Increase the possibilities by using the same vessel in several ways in one year – bulbs in spring and annuals in summer, or else wallflowers, then lilies, followed by late annuals.

V E G E T A B L E S

Good vegetable growing involves a sunny site, good quality soil and forward planning. In small gardens, with a little ingenuity, vegetables can be grown successfully amongst the flowers or in growbags on the patio. In order to keep your plot healthy and to obtain good quality plants, you must work out a rotation of crops so that your vegetables obtain the greatest benefit from the soil available each year. Use this page to write down a general three-year rotation of crops plan, making a careful note of feeding requirements. Enter on the opposite page the vegetables you want to grow in planting order, month by month. Then note the main tasks for their cultivation in the Planner. Later on, it will be great fun, and very good for the ego, to record the harvest in the Monthly Notes.

F R U I T

With a little thought you can grow a wide range of fruit in a small garden. Modern techniques allow for most fruit trees to be grown on dwarf rooting stock, which restricts the size of the fully grown tree. New thornless varieties of blackberry and loganberry make it easier to cultivate soft fruit canes at the rear of flower beds. Have fun covering walls with espaliers and cordons, and double your harvest too. Record here details of the fruit you grow using the sample headings given. Good quality fruit requires some maintenance, so use the Planner to remind yourself of spraying, feeding and pruning times. Use the Monthly Notes to gloat over the harvest.

Name

Source

Date planted/Position/Key no.

Flowering/Fruiting time

Feeding/Pruning/Spraying time

Special needs

H E R B S

Culinary and medicinal herbs have become increasingly popular. Many are highly decorative plants which can be easily grown on small patches of ground, preferably near the kitchen. Alternatively, you can grow them amongst the flowers, in pots on the patio or in charming herb gardens laid out to a pattern. List here the herbs you grow already, and those planned for the future. Try growing them for teas and tisanes.

L A W N S ,   P A T H S   &   P A T I O S

Landscape gardeners maintain that a well-kept lawn does miracles for the average garden. Good lawns need rolling, cutting, weeding, raking, spiking, aerating and feeding at the right time. Use the Planner section to ensure that your lawn gets the best treatment. A special weedkiller used in early spring on paths, patios and drives will give a trouble-free year. Check and maintain fences annually to prolong their usefulness.

L A W N S   &   G R A S S

Date laid

Seed/Turf

Maintenance

T E R R A C E

Date laid

Contractor

Maintenance

PATHS & DRIVES

Date laid

Contractor

Maintenance

FENCES & WALLS

Date erected

Contractor

Maintenance

GARDEN FIXTURES

POTTING SHED

Date bought

Maintenance

_____

_____

_____

_____

_____

_____

_____

_____

_____

_____

_____

_____

_____

_____

_____

GREENHOUSE

Date bought

Heating system

Maintenance

_____

_____

_____

_____

_____

_____

_____

_____

_____

_____

_____

_____

_____

C L O C H E S

Date bought

Maintenance

C O M P O S T

Date started

Additions made

C O N T A I N E R S

Maintenance

A haven from the rain, a storage place for tools, a hidey hole for odds and ends, a shed becomes invaluable in any garden. Briefly outline here details and maintenance requirements of the buildings and structures in your garden. Wooden sheds and greenhouses need to be treated with timber preservative. The glass of greenhouses and frames needs cleaning, while cloches benefit from a good wash and running repairs. Scrub out waterbutts periodically, and check for leakages. Clean out tubs and pots, and then paint or treat wooden ones with preservative. The average decomposition time of a compost heap is six months. Maintaining two heaps – one rotting and one building – will ensure that you have a continuous supply of natural organic food for the garden.

W A T E R B U T T S

Maintenance

Well-kept tools make for easy, pleasurable gardening. Always leave yourself a few minutes at the end of a gardening session to thoroughly clean, and if necessary, to sharpen and oil your tools. Mud-caked, blunt hoes make hard work of weeding. Make a list on this page of all your garden tools and the maintenance they require. Try to note availability of spare parts. It is a good idea to have a record of your leisure equipment such as garden furniture, barbecues, etc, and to note where they were purchased. Space for listing the names and addresses of suppliers is given on the following page.

SUPPLIERS & SUPPLIES

Use this page to keep a note of all the names, addresses and telephone numbers of the many suppliers and experts connected with your garden. Add any comments on their usefulness, and remember to update the information. Joining a local horticultural or allotment society could help you to reduce costs. Make a check list on the opposite page of the main supplies, such as string, stakes, sprays and fertilisers which you need to buy each year. You will find it invaluable at the beginning of each gardening year.

Garden Centres

Seedsmen

Tree Specialists

Landscape Gardeners

Tool Suppliers/Hire

Mail Order Catalogues

Garden Helpers

Horticultural Society

Other

A very pleasant relaxation for busy gardeners is to visit someone else's garden. It is an enjoyable and fruitful way of acquiring new ideas. A small private garden or the garden of a knowledgeable gardening friend can be just as rewarding as a visit to a show garden. The contents of neighbourhood gardens with the same soil and weather conditions as your own should provide numerous good tips. Make a note here of the gardens you have visited or would like to visit, together with any special designs, effects, or flowers which you particularly liked.

There is a tantalizing range of horticultural books and magazines available. This page is to keep track of your favourite gardening publications. Write down those you own and those you would like to possess, stating whether they are useful, inspiring or merely beautiful. You might also like to jot down special quotations which you come across.

PLANTS TO ACQUIRE

_____

_____

_____

_____

_____

_____

_____

_____

_____

_____

_____

_____

_____

_____

_____

_____

_____

_____

_____

_____

_____

_____

_____

_____
_____
_____
_____
_____
_____
_____
_____
_____
_____
_____
_____
_____
_____
_____
_____
_____
_____
_____
_____

Indulge your fantasies on this page. Jot down the names of plants or flowers which you see, read or hear about, and feel you would like to grow. However, before spending your money, be sure that they are suitable for your garden. Keep this book handy while listening to special radio or television programmes. The notes you make will be a helpful reference when planning next year's flower or produce garden.

The purpose of this section is to help you to develop a programme for improving your garden. Use the Inventory and the Monthly Notes as the basis for your plans. The Planner has four pages for each of the busy months. Use the first two for flowers, and the next two for fruit and vegetables. The acompanying notes are for your general guidance only, and you will need to consult your detailed gardening books. Soil and climate vary from district to district, so take this into account when making entries. If there is no heading for the task you wish to do, enter it under General Maintenance, or else make your own separate heading. Try to include something new in your garden each year. Make a systematic sowing plan for vegetable and flower seeds. Provide for the needs of individual plants each month, and do not neglect general maintenance. List also the necessary regular jobs such as weeding and spraying. When you complete a job, make a note of the date and year. Refer back to this section when writing up the Monthly Notes.

JANUARY

Order seeds this month. Check bulbs, tubers and corms in store. If the frost has lifted newly-planted shrubs, tread them in firmly. Warm the soil with cloches, and sow early vegetables. Set first seed potatoes to sprout; plant shallots. Divide, replant and force rhubarb. Apply bonemeal and sulphate of potash to currants, gooseberries and fruit trees. If not already done, complete renewal pruning and spur pruning while fruit trees and bushes are dormant, and follow with a winter wash spray. Remove snow from hedges, shrubs and trees with a long pole.

GENERAL MAINTENANCE

SOWING & PLANTING

 O R D E R I N G

F E E D I N G

S P R A Y I N G

FEBRUARY

Avoid working in the garden when the soil is frozen, wet or sticky. Drain waterlogged soil. Take dahlia and chrysanthemum cuttings. Sow annuals under glass. Feed all established flower beds, and mulch if the weather is favourable. Prune dogwoods. Complete any returfing jobs on the lawn, and apply moss killer. Finish planting fruit trees and bushes. Dress the necessary parts of the vegetable patch with lime, and feed it according to your rotation of crops plan. Sow onions, lettuce, cabbage, carrots and peas.

G E N E R A L
M A I N T E N A N C E

S O W I N G
& P L A N T I N G

1.st   Onions. (Ailsa Craig)
        Tomatoes. (Alicante)
        Cabbage. (Golden Acre)
        Lettuce. (Fortune).
20th planted. Sweet peas
Geraniums. Verbena.
Lobelia. & petunias.

F E E D I N G

1 load of dung.

P R O P A G A T I N G

MARCH

Surface cultivate the warming soil for vegetable seeds and the hardiest annuals – calendulas, candytuft, etc. Plant herbaceous perennials, and also divide and replant old overgrown clumps. Put in deciduous trees and shrubs. Prune shrubs which flower on current year's growth. Prune hybrid, floribunda and miniature roses. Move snowdrops while in leaf. Mulch fruit trees and bushes to preserve moisture, and prune stone fruits as the sap starts to rise. Continue your fruit spraying programme. Stake plants vulnerable to wind. Plant onion sets and maincrop potatoes. Declare war on weeds, and spray drives and paths. Replenish all garden supplies.

GENERAL MAINTENANCE

SOWING & PLANTING

F E E D I N G

P R U N I N G

APRIL

Flowers
Emerging seedlings need to be kept moist. Complete pruning of plants which flower on the current season's growth. Feed and spray roses. After an initial high cut, close cut the lawn and fertilise. List the early flowering shrubs, including heathers, which need pruning now. Plant container-grown shrubs and climbers. Cut hedges well back to encourage dense, leafy growth. Finish sowing annuals. Weed seedlings by hand, and use slug bait judiciously. Plant gladioli corms.

G E N E R A L
M A I N T E N A N C E

S   O   W   I   N   G
&   P   L   A   N   T   I   N   G

P R U N I N G

F E E D I N G

APRIL

Vegetables & Fruit
Keep fruits well watered, weeded and staked. Remove unwanted raspberry suckers, and clean strawberry beds prior to strawing. Watch for pests, and spray regularly, but avoid doing so during bright sunshine when pollinating insects are about. Continue vegetable sowing, both in seedbeds and *in situ*. Under cover sow aubergines, cucumbers, marrows, peppers and tomatoes. Pinch out broad beans when in full flower. Plant out leeks.

GENERAL MAINTENANCE

SOWING & PLANTING

SPRAYING

MAY

Flowers

Plant out fuchsias, hydrangeas and the last of the tender shrubs. Deadhead, lift and store spent bulbs to make space for summer bedding. Harden off young plants properly, and avoid planting them out too early in case of late frosts. Sow half-hardy annuals *in situ*, and biennials in prepared seedbeds. Reduce the number of shoots from the centres of overproductive lupins, delphiniums, phlox and other established perennials, and then stake. Plant hanging baskets. Stake and spray lilies, and guard against slugs. Never let weeds seed themselves and gain control.

GENERAL MAINTENANCE

SOWING & PLANTING

S T A K I N G

M A Y

Vegetables & Fruit
Warm weather brings
aphids and mildew, so
spray regularly. Beware
of gooseberry sawfly.
Remove strawberry
runners, and sow melon
seeds for the coldframe.
Sow vegetables for
continuity – lettuce,
carrots, peas and
beetroot. If the soil is
warm, sow French and
runner beans, sweetcorn
and marrows. Plant out
the first batch of
brassicas. Avoid the
temptation to transplant
tender, tomatoes,
cucumbers, etc. before
the frosts are over. This
is a good time to add
new water plants and to
divide old ones.

G E N E R A L
M A I N T E N A N C E

S O W I N G
& P L A N T I N G

S P R A Y I N G

J U N E

Flowers
Plant out summer bedding after hardening off. Thin seedlings grown *in situ,* and weed well. Prune shrubs which have finished flowering such as weigela and cystus. Take cuttings of rosemary, lavender and other softwoods. Remember that climbers have delicate, easily snapped stems, so provide anchorage for clematis, black-eyed Susan *(thunbergia alata)* and morning glory. Keep the lawn mown and moist. Plant out dahlias with stakes. House plants enjoy an outdoor rain shower on a warm day.

G E N E R A L
M A I N T E N A N C E

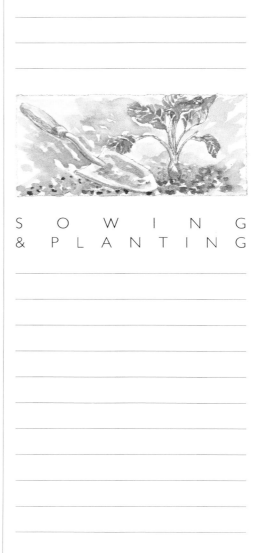

S O W I N G
& P L A N T I N G

P R U N I N G

P R O P A G A T I N G

JUNE

Vegetables & Fruit
Pick gooseberries, currants and strawberries. Spray apples against codling moth. Remove imperfect apples and pears from the trees. Tender vegetables – sweetcorn, cucumbers, runner beans and tomatoes – must be well hardened off before planting out. Earth up maincrop potato tubers. Follow continuity plan for sowing vegetables and salads. Don't forget to hoe. If dry, water frequently and thoroughly. Harvest fresh produce regularly. Keep the compost heap topped up with kitchen and garden waste.

GENERAL
MAINTENANCE

S O W I N G
& P L A N T I N G

S P R A Y I N G

J U L Y

Flowers
Remove faded flowers to
prevent seeds forming
and to extend the
flowering period. This is
the time to trim hedges,
and to prune
philadelphus, deutzia
and other shrubs which
have flowered on one-
year-old wood. Tie in the
rapidly growing shoots
of climbers, and stake
chrysanthemums,
gladioli and perennials.
Thin biennial seedlings
to encourage sturdy
plants. Divide bearded
irises, and plant autumn
crocuses. Water and
fertilise the lawn if
necessary. Routine
weeding is now essential.

G E N E R A L
M A I N T E N A N C E

S O W I N G
& P L A N T I N G

S T A K I N G

P R U N I N G

J U L Y

Vegetables & Fruit
Summer prune restricted
fruit trees – pear and
apple cordons and
espaliers – and
remember to prune
blackcurrants
immediately after
harvesting. Cut out
fruited raspberry canes.
Tidy strawberry beds,
and plant out runners.
Net stone fruit trees
before the birds attack
the fruitlets. Ripen off
Japanese onions, and
continue planting out
late brassicas. Sow peas,
turnips, spinach,
beetroot and lettuce, and
where necessary give
vegetables an additional
feed. Stake and feed
tomatoes, and remove
side shoots. Spray
tomatoes and potatoes
for blight, and runner
beans for blackfly. Water
copiously when dry.

G E N E R A L
M A I N T E N A N C E

S O W I N G
& P L A N T I N G

P R U N I N G

S P R A Y I N G

AUGUST

Flowers
Take cuttings of pelargoniums, penstemons and tender perennials. Prune rambler roses, and finish pruning shrubs that have already flowered. Try using the warm soil to propagate azaleas, rhododendrons and hydrangeas by layering. Regular deadheading encourages new flower growth, so cut your garden flowers and bring them into the house. Plant Madonna lilies, and start cyclamen tubers into growth. Order bulbs for autumn planting and for indoor forcing. Sow hardy annuals this month in order to achieve earlier flowering next year.

GENERAL
MAINTENANCE

SOWING
& PLANTING

P R U N I N G

P R O P A G A T I N G

O R D E R I N G

AUGUST

Vegetables & Fruit
Allow late varieties of apples and pears to develop fully on the tree before storing. Support autumn fruiting raspberries. Use old onion and potato beds to sow Japanese onions, spring cabbage, winter lettuce, parsley, winter spinach, beetroot and turnips. Harvest shallots. Stake Brussels sprouts and broccoli, and watch for white cabbage moth. Stop tomato plants after fourth flower truss, but continue removing side shoots. Harvest fresh produce regularly.

GENERAL
MAINTENANCE

SPRAYING

SOWING
& PLANTING

STAKING

SEPTEMBER

Flowers

Construct or alter rock gardens and pools before the arrival of severe weather. Propagate evergreen shrubs from stem cuttings of current season's growth. Continue to prune rambler and climber roses. Plant out young perennials, and if evergreens need moving, now is the time to transplant them. Pot up bulbs for Christmas flowering. Don't forget to deadhead. Stake tall plants prior to strong winds. Dig new borders or beds early to allow the soil to settle for autumn planting. Rake, spike and top dress the lawn; renovate worn patches with seed or turf.

GENERAL
MAINTENANCE

SOWING
& PLANTING

P R O P A G A T I N G

P R U N I N G

SEPTEMBER

Vegetables & Fruit
Cut out loganberry and autumn fruited raspberry canes, and tie in new canes. Finish pruning currant bushes. Order fruit trees and bushes for planting immediately after leaf fall. Lift maincrop potatoes, dry well and store. Break up grassland and double dig for new vegetable patch. Harvest fresh crops regularly. Collect hydrangea heads and copper beech leaves for drying.

GENERAL MAINTENANCE

SOWING & PLANTING

P R U N I N G

O R D E R I N G

OCTOBER

After the first frosts lift and store dahlias, begonias, gladioli tubers and chrysanthemum stools. Gradually clear spent bedding plants, rake up falling leaves, and store for compost. Try to obtain manure to enrich the compost heap. Plant polyanthus, primroses and biennials in position. Now is the time to plant most hardy bulbs except tulips. When possible, dig over the flower beds, incorporating well rotted compost, and double dig the vegetable patch. Pick tomatoes regularly to allow late formers to develop on the bush. Lift beetroot, carrots and remaining potatoes in advance of frosts.

GENERAL MAINTENANCE

S O W I N G
& P L A N T I N G

F E E D I N G

97

NOVEMBER

Prune deciduous hedges hard to encourage bushy growth. Clean up and thoroughly weed all flower beds, turning over the soil where possible. Cut down herbaceous plants, divide and replant overgrown clumps, and transplant shrubs and perennials as required. Mulch delicate shrubs to protect the roots from frost. Plant tulips, hardy clematis, winter jasmin and honeysuckle. Compost falling leaves and suitable plant remains. Take care to keep pools clean, and check drains and gutters. Spike the lawn to improve structure and drainage. Prune vines immediately after leaf fall, and start pruning apples, pears and blackberries. Complete digging.

GENERAL MAINTENANCE

S O W I N G
& P L A N T I N G

P R U N I N G

DECEMBER

Now is the time to plan for next year. Use your completed Monthly Notes to help you to organise the tasks for produce growing and for your flower beds, and make the entries under the appropriate months in next year's Planner. Use your rotation of crops plan (page 44) in order to devise a systematic sowing and feeding programme for your vegetables. Avoid gardening if the soil is wet or frozen. If necessary, heel in new plants until it is possible to plant them properly. Use straw mulch to protect newly-planted trees and shrubs. Clear under hedges where slugs breed. Prune long rose stems to prevent windrock. Prune fruits before starting your winter spray programme. Remember to have the lawn mower serviced. Check and thoroughly clean all tools. If dry, treat fences and sheds.

GENERAL MAINTENANCE

SOWING & PLANTING

P R U N I N G

S P R A Y I N G

P L A N N I N G

Use this blank page to make new plans or designs. It is easier to be imaginative in your planting schemes if you have worked them out carefully on paper beforehand.

Garden plan (hand-drawn)

- RHUBARB.
- CABBAGE
- RASPBERRIES
- R. BETHS
- LOGANBERRIES
- CAULI FLOWERS ?
- FLOWERS
- RUNNER BEANS
- STRAWBERRIES
- FLOWERS
- RUNNER BEANS
- TOMATOES.
- SMALL SEEDS. CABBAGE ETC.
- Peas
- FRENCH BEANS.
- Shallots & onions.
- Potatoes

103

The purpose of this section is to help you to assess the results of your hard work. Describe monthly how your garden looked, what it produced, and what you enjoyed. The marginal text is intended to make you look carefully and critically at your garden, and to stimulate ideas. For each of the six busy months you have four pages to write in. The headings are to guide you to create a full picture of your garden. Note annual variations in weather and their effects. Under the heading Colour and Contrasts, record what was in flower, and what combinations were effective. What you write under the Produce heading will be useful when making plans for next year. Note the presence of wildlife, whether friend or foe, and measures taken to attract or deter. Assess whether jobs were done at the right time, reasons for successes or failures, and then make suggested improvements for the future. Finally, make use of these notes when filling up the Planner for the following year.

JANUARY

WEATHER

COLOUR & CONTRASTS

106

I M P R O V E M E N T S

W I L D L I F E

P R O D U C E

S P E C I A L   N O T E S

Have you made the most of small flowering bushes this month? Witch-hazel, honeysuckle and winter jasmin add scent and colour to the January garden. Could a display of Christmas roses and the contrasting shapes of dwarf junipers and conifers provide needed interest? Do you have a good supply of Jerusalem artichokes, leeks, winter spinach and Brussels sprouts? In freezing weather, it is vital to give the birds water as well as food.

FEBRUARY

WEATHER

COLOUR & CONTRASTS

IMPROVEMENTS

WILDLIFE

PRODUCE

SPECIAL NOTES

Does your garden resemble an artic waste? You can turn it into a bejewelled winter scene with the help of red-barked dogwoods, variegated ivies, pastel-coloured heathers or scented daphne mezereum. An evergreen clematis lends height and makes an attractive backdrop to snowdrops, winter aconites and iris reticulata. Did your summer planning and planting provide sufficient vegetables to last the winter?

MARCH

COLOUR &
CONTRASTS

I M P R O V E M E N T S

W I L D L I F E

P R O D U C E

S P E C I A L   N O T E S

Do you have any tall flowering shrubs to contrast with low growing bulbs? Would the foliage of golden, variegated or common ivy add a new dimension of texture and colour to your garden? Early rhododendrons bring greenery and height, as well as a splash of colour. Did fences and supports withstand the March gales? Record here the effects you have achieved and notable discrepancies.

111

APRIL

C O L O U R   &
C O N T R A S T S

14th. planted onion sets &
shallots & red onion seed.
21st. put out cabbage plant
& lettuce. planted small
seed, i.e. brussels, cabbage.
flower seed. parsnip &
parsley.
24th. 6 rows of potatoes.

IMPROVEMENTS

Blossoming trees and
shrubs bring exquisite
beauty, and their scent
and colour attract
pollinating bees,
butterflies and other
flying insects.
Ornamental prunus,
forsythia, magnolia and
fritillaries are resplendent
above daffodils,
bergenias and primula
denticulata. Is the rock
garden in full bloom?
Evaluate here the success
and beauty of your early
spring garden.

APRIL

PRODUCE

SPECIAL NOTES

WILDLIFE

Record the first rhubarb picking. With good planning you should now be harvesting asparagus, swiss chard, spinach beet, broccoli, spring greens, turnip tops and spring onions. As the buds burst into leaf, and the fruit buds develop into flowers, look carefully to see if there are enough insects to pollinate the fruit trees. It is useful to record the appearance of frost, which can have a destructive effect on the blossom, and consequently on the crop.

MAY

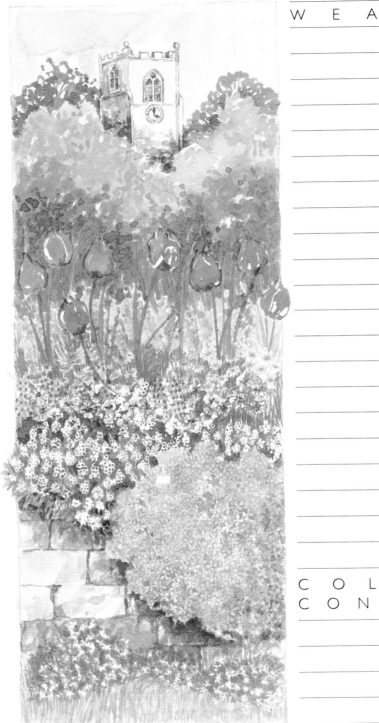

COLOUR &
CONTRASTS

IMPROVEMENTS

Does the emerging beauty of your flower beds include variety of colour, height, scent and texture? Has the bulb display been continuous and satisfactory? Consider whether a focal point or special feature is needed in your garden, for example an early flowering hanging basket. Are your annuals coming along according to schedule, or should you alter your preparation dates?

MAY

SPECIAL NOTES

WILDLIFE

Winter digging should
have resulted in good,
workable soil. Did you
have sufficient compost,
and was it ready on
time? Are you satisfied
with the proportion of
space allotted to fruit,
vegetables and flowers?
Note improvements or
alterations for the future.
Watch out for birds
eating fruit buds.

JUNE

COLOUR &
CONTRASTS

I M P R O V E M E N T S

Has summer's promise of massed vivid colours been fulfilled? Disguise an empty wall or fence with wisteria, clematis, honeysuckle or a rambling rose. Look critically for any gaps where you could grow more biennials – Canterbury bells, foxgloves or wallflowers. Now is the time to sow for next year. Did your early bedding plants survive the late frosts?

121

JUNE

S P E C I A L   N O T E S

W I L D L I F E

It is helpful to note whether tender beans, tomatoes and marrows have survived frost and transplanting. Attract insects to your garden – butterflies love buddleia, and cotoneaster lactus encourages pollinating bees. If any plants look unhappy, note the cause – wrong aspect, incorrect feeding or pruning – and rectify at the right time. Record produce yields with the purpose of increasing them in quality and quantity. Enter arrival date of pests and mildew.

JULY

C O L O U R &
C O N T R A S T S

124

IMPROVEMENTS

How do your rose beds and herbaceous borders compare with the pictures in your special garden books? Try old favourites such as solidago, penstemon and sidalcea, and add summer annuals to make a bold display. Is there a gap for the easily increased regal lilies or shrubs like deutzia, escallonia and lavender? An inverted flower pot on a dahlia stake helps to catch earwigs. Would the introduction of a garden pool bring added pleasure and interest?

JULY

PRODUCE

SPECIAL NOTES

_____

WILDLIFE

_____

Are you enjoying the peak of the summer fruit season? Note whether the quality and quantity of strawberries, raspberries, gooseberries and currants are meeting your requirements. Did you need to follow the June drop of apples and pears with further controlled thinning to improve the crop? Early potatoes and globe artichokes harvested now transform any meal. Make a note of any additional vegetables you would like to grow next year, and remember to transfer this information to the Planner.

127

AUGUST

COLOUR &
CONTRASTS

IMPROVEMENTS

Compare your efforts with the achievements of local parks and keen gardening friends, or peep through fences to see what the neighbours are growing. Note ideas and suggestions for improvements next year. Have you made full use of phlox, gladioli, begonias and early chrysanthemums? Brightly coloured zinnias have a long flowering period in the open, and last well in vases.

AUGUST

SPECIAL NOTES

WILDLIFE

Are you reaping a full harvest of blackberries, loganberries, apples, pears, plums and cherries, or do you want to increase your varieties? Have you enough herbs to create exciting summer salads? It might be fun to experiment with a new herb bed. A record of shallots, onions, tomatoes, peppers and garlic harvested now will simplify your plans for next year's sowing.

SEPTEMBER

COLOUR &
CONTRASTS

IMPROVEMENTS

The length of the summer display will depend mainly on the thoroughness of your deadheading. Are fuchsias, geraniums and Michaelmas daisies still coming into flower? Make notes of suitable plants to extend next year's flowering season. The delicate pink of Japanese anemones enhances colour schemes, and mint-scented eschscholtzia (Californian poppy) adds fragrance. Are the early hydrangea heads ready for drying as indoor decoration?

133

SEPTEMBER

S P E C I A L   N O T E S

W I L D L I F E

The richest harvest of fruit and vegetables is usually found this month. Consider growing luxury fruits such as apricots, nectarines or peaches. Have you been successful in preventing the birds from eating your fruit? Do the trees in your garden give too much shade and need trimming? Record the quantity of maincrop potatoes lifted, and make a note of next year's planting requirements.

OCTOBER

COLOUR &
CONTRASTS

IMPROVEMENTS

WILDLIFE

PRODUCE

SPECIAL NOTES

Does your garden include plants with beautiful autumn foliage such as Virginia creeper and Japanese maple? Look at the splendours in your neighbourhood for inspiration. Would the inclusion of a rock garden with autumn crocus, Neapolitan cyclamen or gentian be an improvement? As winter draws in, remember berry bushes for both beauty and bird food. Have your spring plans resulted in a harvest of first sprouts, parsnips and spinach this month?

NOVEMBER

COLOUR &
CONTRASTS

138

IMPROVEMENTS

WILDLIFE

PRODUCE

SPECIAL NOTES

Is your garden still full of interest? As the leaves fall and plants die back, beauty and colour are found in pyracantha, euonymus and cotoneaster berries as well as exquisite dogwood barks. Violet-coloured aster grandiflora (amellus) will extend your flowering season, contrasting well with the first winter jasmin. Berry fruits are nearly over, but there should still be a good variety of vegetables to harvest. Were the weather and soil suitable for digging?

DECEMBER

COLOUR &
CONTRASTS

I M P R O V E M E N T S

W I L D L I F E

P R O D U C E

S P E C I A L   N O T E S

Do you think you could improve the appearance of your December garden? Heather, mahonia and viburnum make a brave showing in the short winter days. Christmas roses planted near a path enable you to enjoy them without damaging the lawn. This is a good time to review the year's activities, to indulge in some armchair gardening (see page 14), and to inspect stored fruit and vegetables. Finally, go back and complete the gaps in this section, and then start next year's planning.

141